AUTUMN
PUBLISHING

Published in 2020
First published in the UK by Autumn Publishing
An imprint of Igloo Books Ltd
Cottage Farm, NN6 0BJ, UK
Owned by Bonnier Books
Sveavägen 56, Stockholm, Sweden
www.igloobooks.com

© 2019 MARVEL

1220 003
4 6 8 10 9 7 5 3
ISBN 978-1-78905-967-0

Printed and manufactured in China

A GALLERY OF HEROES!

Marvel has a rich history of incredible Super
Heroes. From Super-Soldier Captain America
and tech-genius Iron Man, to the galaxy-travelling
Star-Lord, Peter Quill, to name just a few.

This collection of heroes have always been on hand to
keep Earth, and the rest of the galaxy, safe from the vast
variety of Super Villains that populate the Marvel universe.
Whether villains are seeking to rule the people of Earth,
destroy the galaxy or worse, Super Heroes are always
on hand to stop them and save the day.

In this collection of amazing illustrations, you have
the opportunity to bring the excitement and adventure
of Marvel to life. There are stunning pictures of Black Panther
facing off against the Winter Soldier, Thor fighting to save
Asgard, the Avengers battling cybernetic menace
Ultron, plus many more intricate images.

Whether you want to assemble with the Avengers,
journey with the Guardians of the Galaxy or experience
the weird world of Doctor Strange, every Marvel fan
will enjoy getting creative with this colouring
celebration of Super Heroes!

INVINCIBLE
IRON MAN

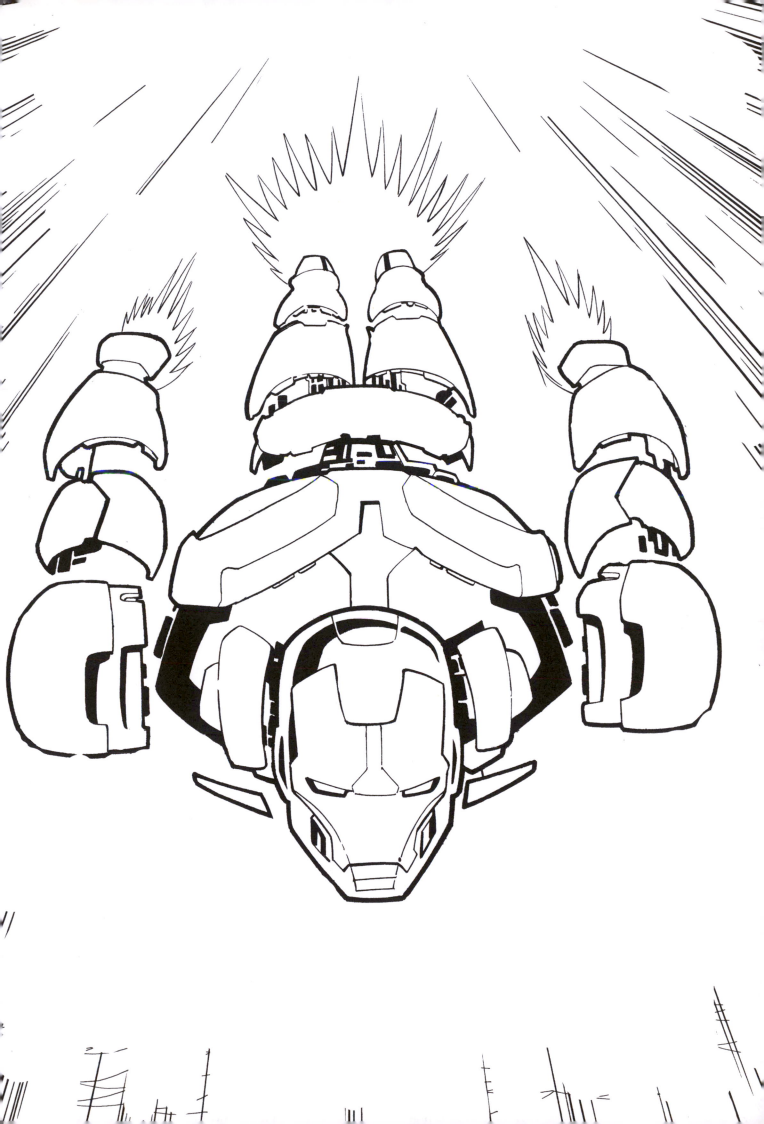

STAR-LORD

GAMORA

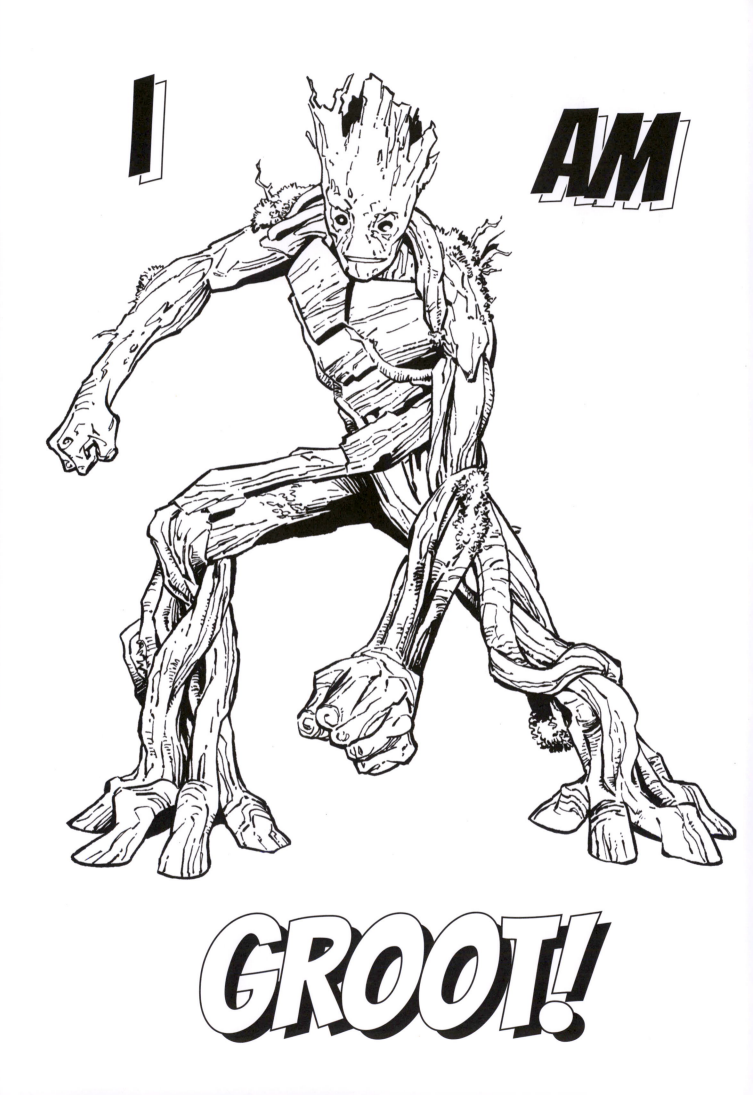

ROCKET

RACCOON

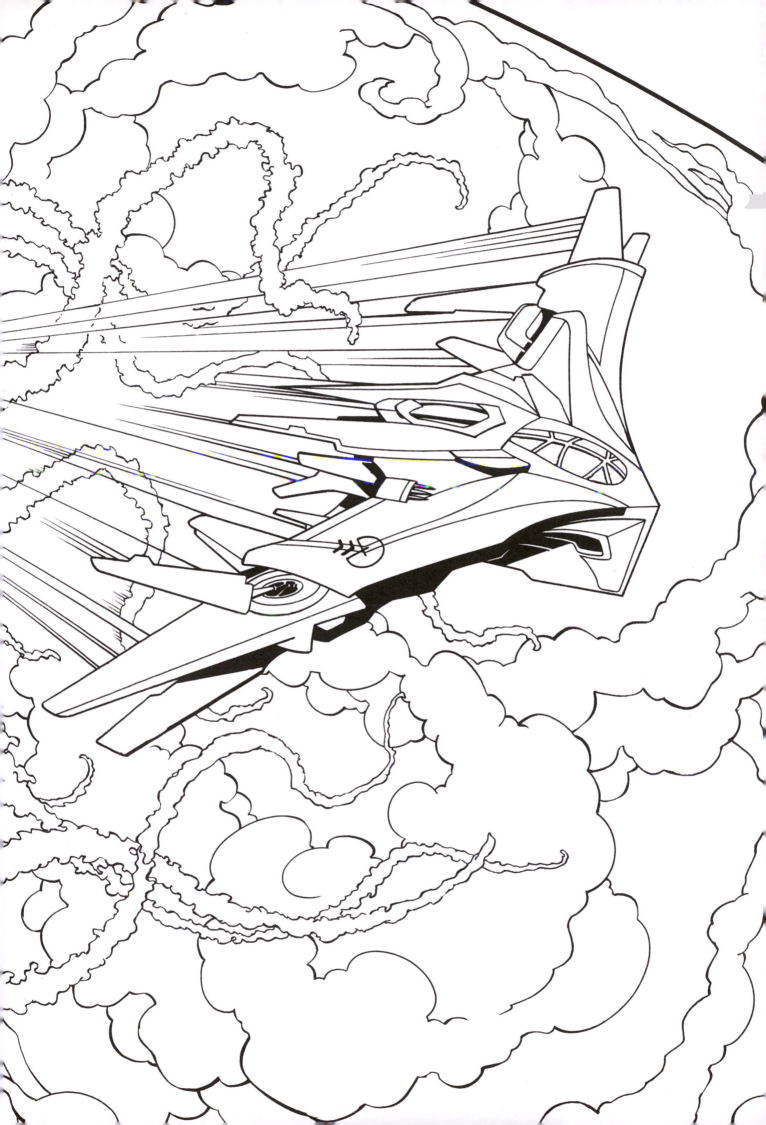

CAPTAIN
AMERICA

HAWKEYE

BLACK

WIDOW

HULK

BUSTER

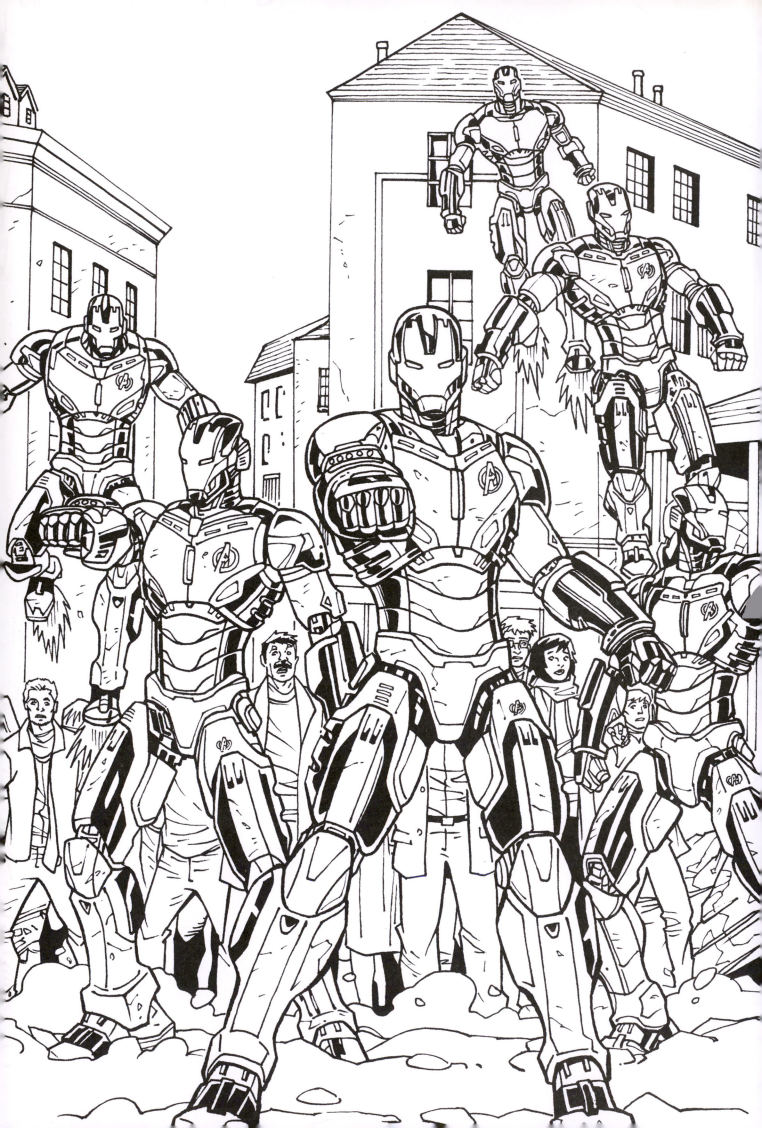

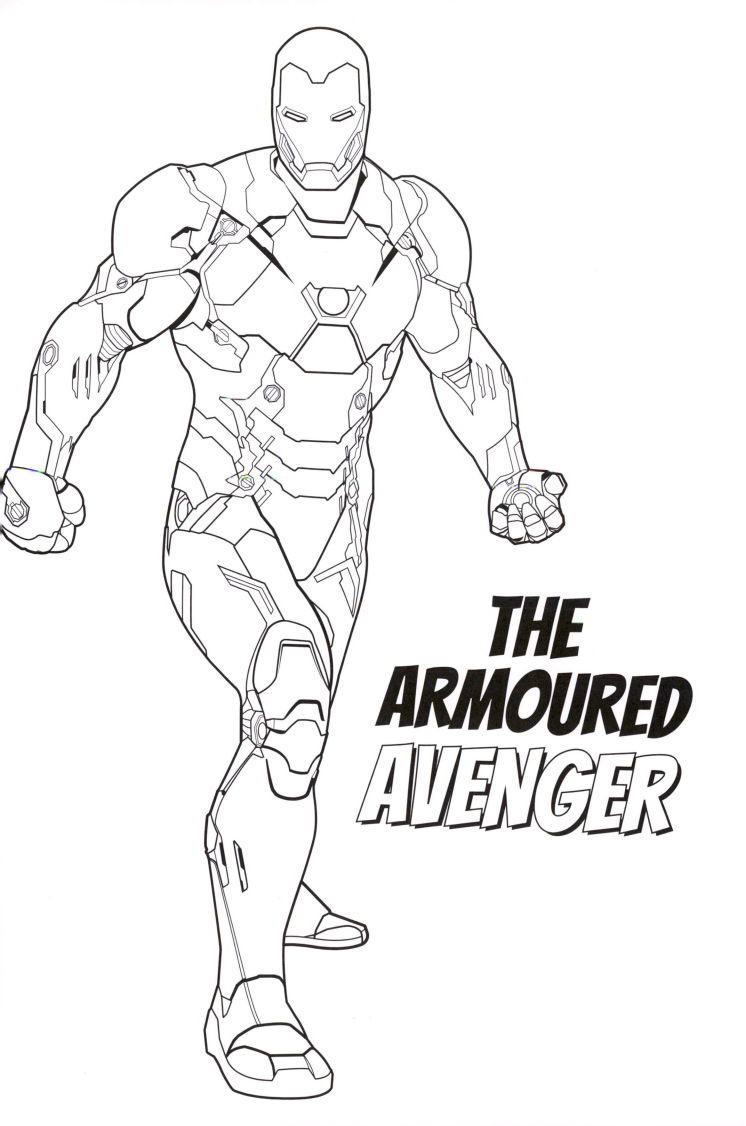

THE
ARMOURED
AVENGER